Naamah and the Ark at Night

a lullaby by SUSAN CAMPBELL BARTOLETTI

illustrated by HOLLY MEADE

CANDLEWICK PRESS

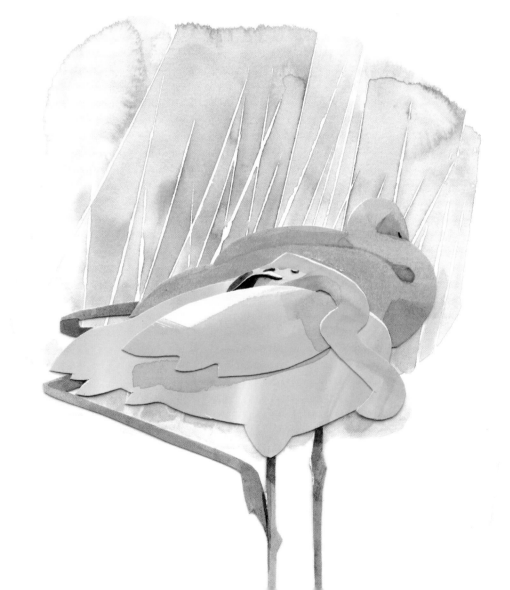

First edition 2011

This edition published specially for The PJ Library® /
The Harold Grinspoon Foundation 2011 by Candlewick Press

Library of Congress Cataloging-in-Publication Data is available.

Library of Congress Catalog Card Number pending

ISBN 978-0-7636-4242-6 (Candlewick hardcover edition)
ISBN 978-0-7636-5768-0 (Harold Grinspoon paperback edition)

11 12 13 14 15 16 SWT 10 9 8 7 6 5 4 3 2 1

Printed in Dongguan, Guangdong, China

This book was typeset in Rialto Piccolo.
The illustrations were done in watercolor collage.

Candlewick Press
99 Dover Street
Somerville, Massachusetts 02144

visit us at www.candlewick.com

For Rocco and Alia, who came two by two,
and Mia, who came by one
S. C. B.

As rain falls over the ark at night,

As water swirls in the dark of night,

As thunder crashes the seams of night,

As Noah tosses in dreams of night,

As restless animals prowl at night,

As they pace and roar and growl at night,

Naamah sings all through the night.

She sings and strokes their hair at night;

She sings a bedtime prayer at night.

She sings for moon to fill the night;

She sings for stars to thrill the night.

She sings for earth and sky at night,

Soothes her sons and their wives at night;

Naamah sings all through the night.

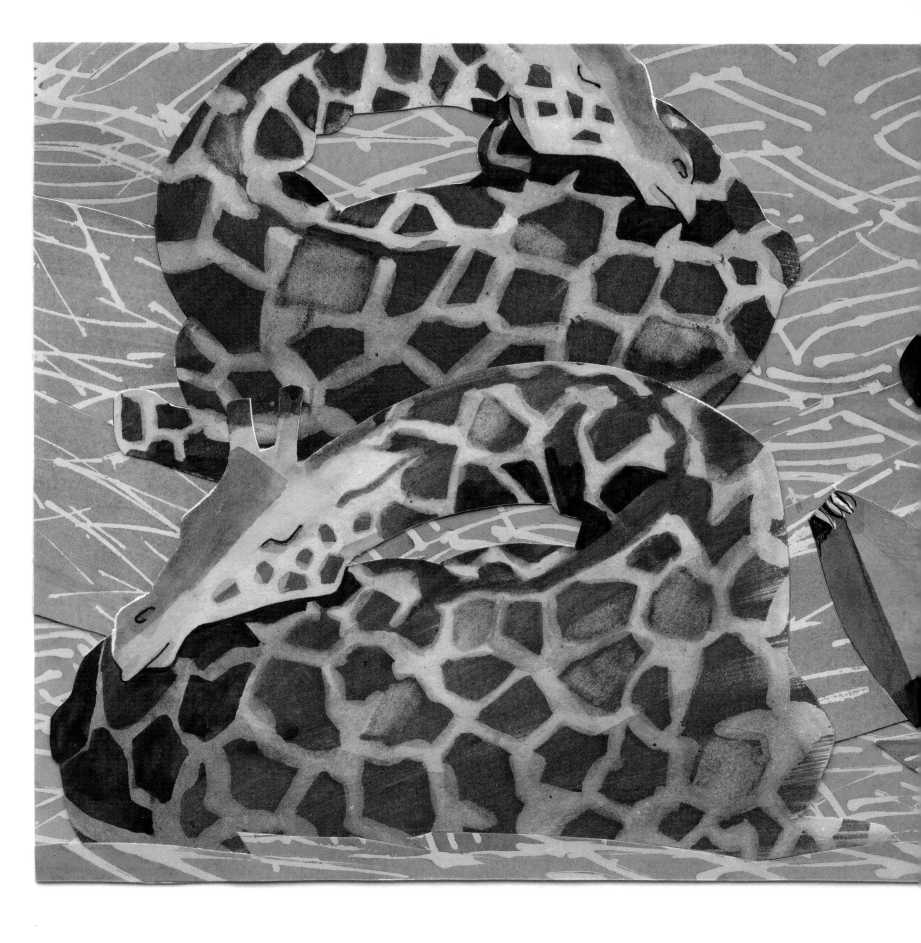

Over the ark, song flows at night.

Two by two, eyes close at night.

Two by two, wings furl at night.

Two by two, tails curl at night.

Two by two, the beasts of night

Are lullabied to sleep at night.

Naamah sings all through the night.

Beneath the clouds that shroud the night,

The ark sails long into the night,

Cradled by the song of night.

Hush hush hush, good night.

Author's Note

As a little girl, when I visited my grandmother, I played with a wooden Noah's ark. I lined up the animals, two by two, and boarded them safely. I imagined the falling rain. I imagined the rising floodwaters. I imagined the ark tossing and turning on the churning sea.

That ark now sits on a shelf in my dining room. All grown up, I no longer play with the ark. I dust it. And as I do, I find that my imagination turns to Noah's wife. In the book of Genesis, we're told that Noah was a just man, full of grace. But what kind of woman was his wife?

The answer may lie in her name. Although an American scholar named Francis Utley listed 103 possible names for Noah's wife in 1941, some rabbinical legends tell us that Noah's wife was called Naamah because her deeds were pleasant. These legends also tell of another Naamah whose name meant "great singer." The name, a variation of the name Naomi (which means "sweet" or "pleasant") is usually given three syllables (Na-ah-mah or Nay-ah-mah).

I like these interpretations of her name. They help me imagine how she inspired and comforted Noah and their three sons and their wives, as well as all the animals. Perhaps Naamah sang.

The form of *Naamah and the Ark at Night* was inspired by a poetic structure called a *ghazal* (sounds like "guzzle"). The *ghazal* is a very old and extremely disciplined Arabic form, dating back to at least the seventh century. Its strict form, usually used in poems about longing and love and loss, requires each couplet to end in the same word, preceded by a rhyming word. An Internet search will help you find more information about the traditional *ghazal*. I thank poet and friend Molly Peacock for introducing me to this form with her sonnet-*ghazal*, "Of Night."

Over the years, Western poets have taken liberty with the traditional *ghazal* form, as I have with *Naamah and the Ark at Night*, a lullaby that I hope inspires readers to trust in the darkness, as Naamah did.